LIVING ON THE EDGE™

FREE ACCESS TO VIDEO

You can stream it for FREE by following the directions below.
Or you can order a DVD at (888) 333-6003 or
LivingontheEdge.org.

YOUR ONLINE CODE

7388071-3SR2-959V

 Please visit LivingontheEdge.org/access and enter this code.

---

3 EASY STEPS

1 | **CREATE AN ACCOUNT**
Go to LivingontheEdge.org/access and complete
the steps to create your FREE account.

2 | **GET IMMEDIATE ACCESS**
Now you will be connected to the resources which
will be needed throughout this workbook.

3 | **ACCESS ANYTIME**
- Log back into your account anytime by visiting
  LivingontheEdge.org and click on STORE.
- From the STORE page, click on Login/Register.
- Enter your login information. Once you are in your
  account, click on MEMBERSHIPS.

Divine Design

Your
DIVINE DESIGN

HOW TO DISCOVER, DEVELOP, AND DEPLOY YOUR SPIRITUAL GIFTS

CHIP INGRAM

Your Divine Design

Table of Contents

How to Start Your Own
Small Group

The fact that you are even reading this page says a lot about you. It says that you are either one of those people that has to read everything, or you are at least open to being used by God to lead a group.

Leading a small group can sound intimidating, but it really doesn't have to be. Think of it more as gathering a few friends to get to know each other better and to have some discussion around spiritual matters.

Here are a few practical tips to help you get started:

1. **Pray**
   One of the most important principles of spiritual leadership is to realize you can't do this on your own. No matter how long we've been leading, we need the power of the Holy Spirit. Lean on Him... He will help you.

2. **Invite some friends**
   Don't be afraid to ask people to come to your group. You will be surprised how many people are open to such a study, especially when you let them know that the study is only for eight weeks. Whether you have 4 of 14 in your group, it can be a powerful experience. You should probably plan on at least an hour and a half for your group meeting.

3. **Get your materials**
   You will need to get a DVD of the video teaching done by Chip Ingram. You can get the DVD from LivingontheEdge.org. Also, it will be helpful for each person to have their own study guide. You can also purchase those through the website.

4. **Be prepared to facilitate**
   Just a few minutes a week in preparation can make a huge difference in the group experience. Each week preview the video teaching and review the discussion questions. If you don't think your group can get through all the questions, select the ones that are most relevant to your group.

5. **Love your group**
   Maybe the most important thing you bring to the group is your personal care for them. If you will pray for them, encourage them, call them, e-mail them, involve them, and love on them, God will be pleased and you will have a lot of fun along the way.

How to Get the Most Out of This
Experience

You and your group are about to begin what could be a life-changing journey in your small group. This powerful study of Your Divine Design provides some breakthrough teaching that will not only help your group discover their gifts but also learn how to develop and deploy them.

Listed below are the segments you will experience each week as well as some hints for getting the most out of this experience.

TAKE IT IN: During this section you will watch the video teaching. Each teaching segment is about 20 minutes long. A teaching outline with fill-ins is provided for each session. As you follow along, write down questions or insights that you can share during the discussion time. Also, bring your Bible each week.

TALK IT OVER: Several discussion questions are provided for your group to further engage the teaching content. Keep the following guidelines in mind for having a healthy group discussion.

- **Be involved.** Jump in and share your thoughts. Your ideas are important, and you have a perspective that is unique and can benefit the other group members.

- **Be a good listener.** Value what others are sharing. Seek to really understand the perspective of others in your group and don't be afraid to ask follow up questions.

- **Be courteous.** Always treat others with utmost respect. When there is disagreement, focus on the issue and never turn the discussion into a personal attack.

- **Be focused.** Stay on topic. Help the group explore the subject at hand, and try to save unrelated questions or stories for afterwards.

- **Be careful not to dominate.** Be aware of the amount of talking you are doing in proportion to the rest of the group, and make space for others to speak.

- **Be a learner.** Stay sensitive to what God might be wanting to teach you through the lesson, as well as through what others have to say.

LIVE IT OUT: These simple suggestions help the lesson come to life. Don't ignore them; give them a try! Check in with another group member during the week and ask how it's going.

How to Utilize Resources
Overview

This teaching is available in both audio and video formats. The DVD resource is designed to have a personal study guide accompany the DVD teaching. Each session corresponds to a specific section in the study guide to be used as a viewer's guide for taking video notes during the DVD teaching. Talk-it-Over questions and Live-it-Out applications are available at the end of each session for personal reflection and/or group discussions.

For Leaders of the group study a leader's guide can be found in the back of each study guide. This section contains tips for preparing and facilitating discussions. The session notes are brief highlights to aid in preparing for each week's lessons. There is also "Coaching for Leaders" at www.livingontheedge.org; click on the Group Studies tab; Q&A videos provide insight and support for small group facilitators.

Free "Message Notes" are available for use with the audio formats—CD or MP3. From our home page www.livingontheedge.org; click on broadcast; click on message notes. Scroll to find the message notes link. Message notes can be printed and copied for additional use.

Session
ONE

YOU'RE A MASTERPIECE IN THE MAKING

PART 1

DEFINITION OF A MAKEOVER

"Makeover is a process of taking something that is old, broken, imperfect, damaged or not useful and recreating it into something that is whole, useful, beautiful, attractive and new."

What attracts us to a makeover?

- We all love to see _____ .

- Our curiosity is riveted by the skill and creativity involved in making the old, new and the broken, whole.

- All of us secretly long for an extreme makeover in some area of our lives or relationships.

THE ULTIMATE EXTREME MAKEOVER

2 CORINTHIANS 5:17 (NIV)

[17]Therefore, if anyone is in Christ, he is a new creation; the old has gone, the new has come!

HOW DOES GOD DO AN EXTREME MAKEOVER?

- Who you _____

EPHESIANS 2:1-3 (NIV)

[1]As for you, you were dead in your transgressions and sins, [2]in which you used to live when you followed the ways of this world and of the ruler of the kingdom of the air, the spirit who is now at work in those who are disobedient. [3]All of us also lived among them at one time, gratifying the cravings of our sinful nature and following its desires and thoughts. Like the rest, we were by nature objects of wrath.

- ○ Dead in our transgressions

- ○ We are prisoners of the world system

- ○ We are objects of wrath

- Who you are _____

EPHESIANS 2:4-6 (NIV)

> [4]But because of his great love for us, God, who is rich in mercy, [5]made us alive with Christ even when we were dead in transgressions—it is by grace you have been saved. [6]And God raised us up with Christ and seated us with him in the heavenly realms in Christ Jesus,

- Why does God do extreme makeovers?

EPHESIANS 2:7-9 (NIV)

> [7]in order that in the coming ages he might show the incomparable riches of his grace, expressed in his kindness to us in Christ Jesus. [8]For it is by grace you have been saved, through faith—and this not from yourselves, it is the gift of God— [9]not by works, so that no one can boast.

- Extreme makeovers are done by God, not by us and our
_____ .

- You are a _____ in the making.

EPHESIANS 2:10 (NIV)

> For we are God's workmanship, created in Christ Jesus to do good works, which God prepared in advance for us to do.

🗩 TALK IT OVER

1. Who is a person that you know who has been radically changed by Jesus Christ? They had an extreme makeover. What was the biggest change you saw in them?

   _____

   _____

2. Ephesians 2:1-3 describes our condition before Jesus did a makeover in our lives.

   Share a little about your life before Christ. What caused you to see your sinfulness and need for Christ?

   _____

   _____

3. Take some time to have some of the people in your group share their personal conversion story.

   _____

   _____

4. How is your life different because Jesus did a makeover in you?

   Share a couple of ways in which you have experienced God's grace and blessings since you became a Christ follower.

   _____

   _____

5. Ephesians 2:10 says that you are God's workmanship (his masterpiece). You are a canvas on which God is painting a priceless piece of art. What work is God doing now in your life?

   _____

   _____

6.   Share what you hope to get out of this study.

_____

_____

☻ LIVE IT OUT

1.   Write a letter of gratitude to God thanking Him for what He did in saving you and how He has changed your life.

2.   Write an e-mail or letter to somebody letting them know how you have seen God change them and how they are a masterpiece that God is making.

Session
TWO

PART 2

Where does God do his "extreme makeover"?

EPHESIANS 2:18-22 (NIV)

[18]For through him we both have access to the Father by one Spirit. [19]Consequently, you are no longer foreigners and aliens, but fellow citizens with God's people and members of God's household, [20]built on the foundation of the apostles and prophets, with Christ Jesus himself as the chief cornerstone. [21]In him the whole building is joined together and rises to become a holy temple in the Lord. [22]And in him you too are being built together to become a dwelling in which God lives by his Spirit.

- In a special house (of God)... the _____

EPHESIANS 3:10-12 (NIV)

[10]His intent was that now, through the church, the manifold wisdom of God should be made known to the rulers and authorities in the heavenly realms, [11]according to his eternal purpose which he accomplished in Christ Jesus our Lord. [12]In him and through faith in him we may approach God with freedom and confidence.

EPHESIANS 3:14-19 (NIV)

[14]For this reason I kneel before the Father, [15]from whom his whole family in heaven and on earth derives its name. [16]I pray that out of his glorious riches he may strengthen you with power through his Spirit in your inner being, [17]so that Christ may dwell in your hearts through faith. And I pray that you, being rooted and established in love, [18]may have power, together with all the saints, to grasp how wide and long and high and deep is the love of Christ, [19]and to know this love that surpasses knowledge—that you may be filled to the measure of all the fullness of God.

- In the _____

How does God do extreme makeovers?

EPHESIANS 4:7-13 (NIV)

---

[7]But to each one of us grace has been given as Christ apportioned it. [8]This is why it says:

"When he ascended on high,

he led captives in his train

and gave gifts to men."[9](What does "he ascended" mean except that he also descended to the lower, earthly regions? [10]He who descended is the very one who ascended higher than all the heavens, in order to fill the whole universe.) [11]It was he who gave some to be apostles, some to be prophets, some to be evangelists, and some to be pastors and teachers, [12]to prepare God's people for works of service, so that the body of Christ may be built up [13]until we all reach unity in the faith and in the knowledge of the Son of God and become mature, attaining to the whole measure of the fullness of Christ.

•   The evidence of Christ's victory over Satan, death, and sin is the deposit of _____ in the church.

How did Christ give spiritual gifts?

By the ascended Christ, to every believer,

For the profit of others,

Through the Holy Spirit sovereignly;

At the time of salvation, on the basis of grace,

To produce the life of Christ (the "Ultimate Makeover")

In every believer

TEN PRINCIPLES FOR UNDERSTANDING SPIRITUAL GIFTS

1. Every Christian has one or more spiritual gifts.

2. Many believers have received more than one spiritual gift.

3. Spiritual gifts are given at the moment of regeneration, but they may lie undiscovered and dormant for a long period of time.

4. Spiritual gifts can be abused and neglected, but if they are received at regeneration, it would appear that they cannot be lost.

5. Spiritual gifts are not the same as the gift of the Holy Spirit.

6. Spiritual gifts are not the same as the fruit of the Spirit.

7. Spiritual gifts are not the same as natural talents.

8. Some spiritual gifts are more useful in local churches than others because they result in greater edification of the body.

9. Charismata literally means "grace gifts". These gifts are sovereignly and undeservedly given by the Holy Spirit.

10. Gifts are God's spiritual equipment for effective service and edification of the body.

⁉ TALK IT OVER

1. Go back to Ephesians 2:18-22 and read the passage again. Then, share about somebody God has used to build and shape your life.

_____

_____

2. From Ephesians 2:18-22, what can we learn about the church and what the church is supposed to be?

_____

_____

3. Read Ephesians 3:14-19. How is this prayer different from those we typically hear from Christians?

_____

_____

4. Make a list of the things that Paul prays for in Ephesians 3:14-19. Which one is most what you need right now?

_____

_____

5. Describe a time when you have benefited or been helped by somebody exercising their gift.

_____

_____

6. Look over the 10 Principles of Understanding Spiritual Gifts. Do any of them surprise you? If so, which one and why?

_____

_____

☙ LIVE IT OUT

1. Review the 10 principles for understanding spiritual gifts before coming next week.

2. Spend a few minutes with someone you know who is using their spiritual gifts to serve others. Find out how they discovered their gifts and started using them.

HOW TO DISCOVER YOUR PRIMARY SPIRITUAL GIFT

PART 1

You are a paintbrush. God uses the paintbrush in your hand (your gifts) to help change and transform others in the body of Christ. And God uses others in your life to make you like Christ.

THE SPIRITUAL GIFT JOURNEY

○ The era of _____

○ The era of _____

○ The era of _____

○ The era of _____

TEN PRINCIPLES FOR UNDERSTANDING SPIRITUAL GIFTS

1. Every Christian has one or more spiritual gifts.

2. Many believers have received more than one spiritual gift.

3. Spiritual gifts are given at the moment of regeneration, but they may lie undiscovered and dormant for a long period of time.

4. Spiritual gifts can be abused and neglected, but if they are received at regeneration, it would appear that they cannot be lost.

5. Spiritual gifts are not the same as the gift of the Holy Spirit.

6. Spiritual gifts are not the same as the fruit of the spirit.

7. Spiritual gifts are not the same as natural talents.

8. Some spiritual gifts are more useful in local churches than others because they result in greater edification of the body.

9. Charismata literally means "grace gifts". These gifts are sovereignly and undeservedly given by the Holy Spirit.

10. Gifts are God's spiritual equipment for effective service and edification of the body.

People often look at spiritual gifts as a kind of spiritual salad bar.

But it has little or no impact on how they actually live the Christian life.

THE FRAMEWORK – 4 BASIC PASSAGES

- Romans 12
- I Corinthians 12
- Ephesians 4
- I Peter 4

The critical question: How do you _____
the gifts talked about in these 4 passages?

1 CORINTHIANS 12:4-6 (NIV)

There are different kinds of gifts, but the same Spirit. [5]There are different kinds of service, but the same Lord. [6]There are different kinds of working, but the same God works all of them in all men.

THE FRAMEWORK – I CORINTHIANS 12:4-6 (NIV)

"GIFTS" Motivational *Rom. 12*	"SERVICE" Ministry *Eph. 4/I Cor. 12:28*	"WORKINGS" Manifestation *I Cor. 12:8-11*
• Prophecy	• Apostles	• Word of Wisdom
• Service	• Prophets	• Word of Knowledge
• Teaching	• Evangelists	• Faith
• Encouragement	• Pastor/Teacher	• Healing
• Giving	• Teachers	• Miracles
• Leadership	• Working of Miracles	• Prophecy
• Mercy	• Gifts of Healing	• Discernment
	• Helping	• Tongues
	• Tongues	• Interpretation of Tongues
	• Administration	

3 KINDS OF SPIRITUAL GIFTS

1. Every believer has one primary _____ gift
   (Romans 12:6-8)

2. That motivational gift can express itself through a variety of
   _____ gifts (Eph. 4 and 1 Cor. 12:28ff)

3. When we exercise our motivational gift through our ministry gift the
   Holy Spirit determines what _____ or impact
   the believer will receive. (1 Cor. 12:8-11)

ROMANS 12:6-8 (NIV)

⁶We have different gifts, according to the grace given us. If a man's gift is prophesying, let him use it in proportion to his faith. ⁷If it is serving, let him serve; if it is teaching, let him teach; ⁸if it is encouraging, let him encourage; if it is contributing to the needs of others, let him give generously; if it is leadership, let him govern diligently; if it is showing mercy, let him do it cheerfully.

As you go through the bible you discover that we are commanded to do all 7 of these motivational gifts. And every church needs these 7 things and every believer needs these 7 in order to fully grow.

So, out of a servant's heart, we will exercise all 7 of these things, but there is one area where we are most gifted and that is where we need to _____ our effort.

THE WAY YOU EXPERIENCE YOUR GIFTEDNESS

- The fulfillment factor

- The fruitfulness factor

🗨 TALK IT OVER

1. When it comes to serving, describe a time or experience when you felt most fulfilled?

_____

_____

2. Think back to Chip's personal testimony. Which era are you in right now? Ignorance, Confusion, Discovery, and Convergence?

_____

_____

3. Why do you think so many people never move beyond discovery to actually using their gifts?

_____

_____

4. Chip said that many Christians look at spiritual gifts as a kind of spiritual salad bar. What are some potential problems with this approach to gifts?

_____

_____

5. What new insight did you get about spiritual gifts from Chip's teaching?

_____

_____

6. Review the seven motivational gifts. At this point, which one most seems like it would describe your gifting.

_____

_____

☺ LIVE IT OUT

Do a little survey this week of 3 people that know you well. Ask them this question; "As you have observed me, where do you think I am most gifted?"

Session
FOUR

PART 2

7 MOTIVATIONAL GIFTS (ROMANS 12)

Prophecy   ○ Yes   ○ No   ○ Maybe

The divine enablement to proclaim God's truth with power and clarity in a timely and culturally sensitive fashion for correction, repentance and edification. It's the ability to reveal God's word accurately.

Intuitive question: What went wrong?

The primary nature of prophecy is forthtelling and accurate teaching of God's word. It's the ability and consuming desire to reveal the truth of God that it might impact lives.

CHARACTERISTICS OF PROPHECY

- Tend to be persuasive speakers
- Can read people
- Often are opinionated
- Like large groups rather than one on one

DANGERS

- Can be proud of their speaking ability
- Dependent on speaking ability rather than power of the Holy Spirit
- Insensitive to the feelings of other people

Service   ○ Yes   ○ No   ○ Maybe

The divine enablement to attach spiritual value to the accomplishment of physical tasks within the body of Christ. It's the ability to demonstrate love by meeting practical needs that releases other Christians for direct spiritual ministry.

Intuitive question: What can I do to help?

CHARACTERISTICS

- Doesn't need much public recognition
- Don't seek the limelight
- Content to work behind the scenes
- Often likes manual projects
- Unusual ability to detect people's personal needs
- Able to overlook personal discomfort to meet people's needs

DANGERS

- Can be bitter when their deeds are not recognized
- Putting an overemphasis on practical needs to the exclusion of spiritual needs

Teaching    ○ Yes   ○ No   ○ Maybe

The divine enablement to understand and give detailed explanation of biblical truth. It's the ability to search out and validate truth which has been presented.

Intuitive question: What is truth?

CHARACTERISTICS

- Love to do research
- Very content and doctrinally oriented

DANGERS

- Concentrate too much on content to the exclusion of application

- Boasting or getting proud about their knowledge

- Being inattentive to responsive students

Exhortation

O Yes   O No   O Maybe

The divine enablement to come alongside another in need of encouragement to reassure, strengthen, affirm, and challenge those who are discouraged or wavering in their faith. It's the ability to stimulate the faith of others.

Intuitive question: What must be done to fix this? And How can we move this person to wholeness?

CHARACTERISTICS

- Gifted in counseling

- See practical application in scripture

- They call us to godly living

- They initiate, implore, request, entreat

DANGERS

- Spend too much time with people who only want temporary solutions to their problems

- Can become discouraged from lack of results of people they are ministering to

Giving

O Yes   O No   O Maybe

The divine enablement to earn money, manage it well and wisely contribute to the work of the Lord with cheerfulness and liberality. It's the ability to entrust personal assets to others for the furtherance of their ministry.

Intuitive question: What can I give to meet the needs?

CHARACTERISTICS

- Don't like limelight
- Like to give anonymously
- Want to know the ROI on their giving
- Hate high pressure tactics
- Don't have to be wealthy

DANGERS

- Can have a tendency to be prideful
- Overemphasizing material needs to the exclusion of spiritual needs
- Judging others spiritually by their bank account

Leadership   O Yes   O No   O Maybe

The divine enablement to see what needs to be done, set goals and attract, and lead and motivate people to accomplish the work of the ministry. Ability to coordinate the activities of others for the achievement of common goals.

Intuitive question: What's the goal?

CHARACTERISTICS

- Gives vision and direction
- Can mobilize other people
- Ability to delegate and take charge
- Enjoy responsibility
- See how things fit together
- People are attracted to them

DANGERS

- Can use people to achieve their goals
- Can get proud or pushy with the power that is given them
- Sometimes forget the purpose of the project

Mercy   O Yes   O No   O Maybe

The divine enablement to minister cheerfully and appropriately to people who are suffering or undeserving and to spare them from punishment or consequences they justly deserve. It's the ability to identify with and comfort those who are in distress.

Intuitive question: How can I make them feel better?

CHARACTERISTICS

- Able to detect and discern people's feelings
- Very sensitive to the point of action
- Want direct personal ministry

DANGERS

- Tend to have a hard time being firm when necessary
- Resentment of those who don't have this gift
- Often misunderstood by people of the opposite sex

⟩⟩ TALK IT OVER

1. Which one of those 7 responses in the story most describes you? If you had been there, what would have been your most natural response?

   _____

   _____

2. From this week's teaching, what new insight did you get into what is your primary motivational gift?

   _____

   _____

3. Which of the characteristics that Chip listed from your motivational gift most describe you?

   _____

   _____

4. Which of the dangers do you most need to be aware of?

   _____

   _____

5. Share a story from your past that would give indication of your primary spiritual gift?

   _____

   _____

6. How should understanding your primary motivational gift impact you?

   _____

   _____

❂ LIVE IT OUT

Copy down the definition of the gift that you believe could be your primary motivational gift. Review it several times this week and then do a MORE—LESS exercise. Take a sheet of paper and draw a line down the middle. At the top of one column put the word MORE. At the top of the other column put the word LESS. Then, make a list in each column of your answers to the following questions: "If this really is my gift, I should spend MORE time..." And "if this really is my gift, I should spend LESS time..."

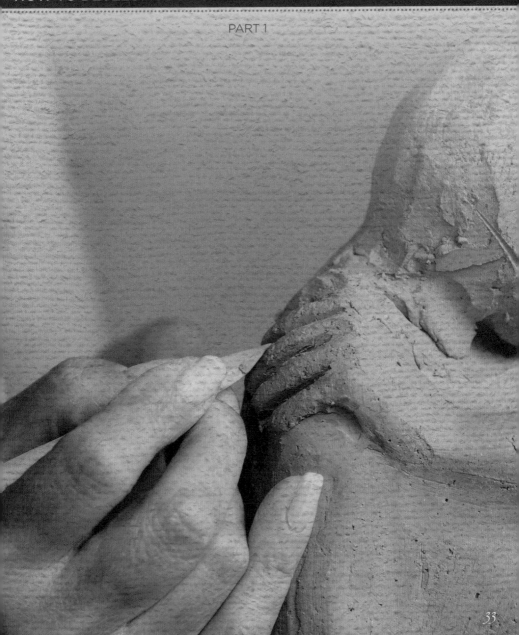

Session
FIVE

PART 1

DEVELOPING YOUR MINISTRY GIFTS (EPH. 4 & 1 COR. 12:28)

5 REASONS YOU NEED TO DEVELOP YOUR SPIRITUAL GIFT

- Direction and _____ for your life.

- Freedom to embrace and enjoy _____.

- The _____ that results from impacting lives.

- Affirmation of your _____ with Christ

- Accountability as you will be held responsible for the _____ of your gift.

1. Developing your gifts begins with _____

   There are three types of spiritual gifts—

   - Every believer has one primary motivational gift (Romans 12:6-8). We are to concentrate on discovering and developing this gift.

   - That motivational gift (drive and ability) can express itself through a variety of ministry gifts. (1 Corinthians 12:28; Ephesians 4:11)

   - When we exercise our motivational gift through our ministry gifts, the Holy Spirit determines what manifestations (or effects) will most benefit people. (1 Corinthians 12:7)

1 CORINTHIANS 12:4-6 (NIV)

There are different kinds of gifts, but the same Spirit. There are different kinds of service, but the same Lord. There are different kinds of working, but the same God works all of them in all men.

"GIFTS"	"SERVICE"	"WORKINGS"
Motivational	Ministry	Manifestation
Rom. 12	*Eph. 4/I Cor. 12:28*	*I Cor. 12:8-11*
• Prophecy	• Apostles	• Word of Wisdom
• Service	• Prophets	• Word of Knowledge
• Teaching	• Evangelists	• Faith
• Encouragement	• Pastor/Teacher	• Healing
• Giving	• Teachers	• Miracles
• Leadership	• Working of Miracles	• Prophecy
• Mercy	• Gifts of Healing	• Discernment
	• Helping	• Tongues
	• Tongues	• Interpretation of Tongues
	• Administration	

1 CORINTHIANS 12:7 (NIV)

Now to each one the manifestation of the Spirit is given for the common good

Your gifts have been given to _____ other people.

2. Developing your gifts demands a basic _____ of the New Testament gifts

Apostleship

The divine enablement to start churches or other ministries and oversee their development. The ability to minister cross-culturally with the goal of planting churches.

Prophecy

The divine enablement to proclaim God's truth with power and clarity in a timely and culturally sensitive fashion. The focus is for correction, repentance, or edification. It's the ability to reveal God's Word accurately.

Evangelism

The ability to be an unusually effective instrument in leading unbelievers to a saving knowledge of Christ. Some with this gift are most effective in personal evangelism, while others may be used by God in group evangelism or cross-cultural evangelism.

Pastor/Teacher

A person with this spiritual gift has the ability to lead, nourish, protect, and personally care for the needs of a "flock" of believers. Not all people with the office of pastor (elder, overseer) have or need the gift of pastoring or shepherding, and many with this gift do not have or need the office. This gift also includes teaching ability and is the only dual gift in the list.

Teaching

The divine enablement to understand and give detailed explanation of biblical truth. Ability to search out and validate truth which has been presented.

Miracles

The ability to serve as an instrument through whom God accomplishes acts that manifest supernatural power. Miracles bear witness to the presence of God and the truth of his proclaimed Word and appear to occur most frequently in association with missionary activity. The gospel message carries its own authority, but God sometimes graciously uses miracles to authenticate and open doors for the proclamation of forgiveness and life in Christ.

Healing

The ability to serve as a human instrument through whom God cures illnesses and restores health. The possessor of this gift is not the source of power but a vessel who can heal only those diseases the Lord chooses to heal. This spiritual gift should not be confused with the signs and wonders performed by Jesus and the apostles, and it should not be discredited because of the abuses of grandstanding faith healers.

🗩 TALK IT OVER

1. Describe a time when you feel like God used you?

    _____

    _____

2. In churches you've attended, how important was the discovery and development of spiritual gifts?

    _____

    _____

3. Which of the 5 reasons for developing your gifts most motivates you?

    _____

    _____

4. Read about the Judgment Seat of Christ in I Corinthians 3:10-15 and 2 Corinthians 5:6-10. What can we learn from these two passages about our accountability for the stewardship of our gifts?

    _____

    _____

5. Chip talked about the need for clarity. What happens in our lives when we are not clear about who we are or what gifts we have?

   What is the negative by-product?

   _____

   _____

6. Of the gifts Chip has described so far, is there one that fits you? (If not, don't worry. Chip will explain the rest during the next session.)

   _____

   _____

☺ LIVE IT OUT

Think about someone whose spiritual gift has helped and blessed you. Get in touch with them this week and thank them for using their gifts and for impacting your life.

Session
SIX

PART 2

Helps

The ability to enhance the effectiveness of a ministry or members of the body. This is the only use of this word in the NT and it appears to be distinct from the gift of service. Some writers suggest that while the gift of service is more group oriented the gift of helps is more person oriented.

Administration/Leadership

This word only appears once in the New Testament and is used outside of scripture for the helmsman who steers a ship toward its destination. This suggests that the spiritual gift of administration is the ability to steer a church or Christian organization toward the fulfillment of its goals by managing its affairs and implementing necessary plans. A person may have the gift of leadership without the gift of administration.

The gift of leadership often asks the "what" question. The gift of administration asks the "how" question.

One of the indicators of your spiritual gift is what comes so natural and easy for you. A clue to your spiritual gift is seen in your _____ to things.

THE MANIFESTATION (WORKINGS) OF YOUR GIFTS

Wisdom

The ability to apply the principles of God's word in a practical way to specific situations and then to recommend the best course of action at the best time. The exercise of this gift skillfully distils insight and discernment into excellent advice.

Knowledge

The ability to discover and analyze and systemize truth for the benefit of others. With this gift one speaks with understanding and penetration. But the word of knowledge can also involve supernatural perception and discernment for the purpose of ministering to others.

Faith

The ability to have a vision for what God wants done and to believe confidently that it will be accomplished in spite of circumstances and appearance to the contrary. The gift of faith transforms vision into reality.

Distinguishing of Spirits (Discernment)

The ability to discern the spirit of truth from the spirit of error. With this gift one may distinguish reality versus counterfeits, the divine versus the demonic, and true versus false teaching, and in some cases, spiritual versus carnal motives.

Tongues

The ability to receive and impart a spiritual message in a language the recipient has never learned so that other members of the body may be edified. This message must be interpreted either by the recipient or by another person with the gift of interpretation.

Interpretation of Tongues

This is the God given ability to translate in a language the recipient doesn't know.

3. Developing your spiritual gifts demands that you exercise them by involvement in...

- People's lives and _____

- A _____ community

- _____ training and education

- Regular _____ opportunities

⏸ TALK IT OVER
···

1. How could your gifts help your small group? And, how could the gifts of others help you?

   _____

   _____

2. Chip said One of the indicators of your spiritual gift is what comes so natural and easy for you. A clue to your spiritual gift is seen in your reaction to things. What do you react against that might be an indicator of your spiritual gifting?

   _____

   _____

3. Who do you know that has the gift of wisdom? How have you benefited from their gift of wisdom?

   _____

   _____

4. Developing your spiritual gift means getting involved with people. Where could you use your gift that would get you involved in the lives of people? Be specific.

   _____

   _____

5. How engaged are you in a small group community? This is far more than just attending a group, it is sharing life with a few people. What would take your group to a deeper level of sharing life together?

   _____

   _____

6. Developing your gift is like exercising a muscle and includes ongoing training and education. What kind of training could help you strengthen your gift?

_____

_____

✪ LIVE IT OUT

Developing your spiritual gifts means taking risks. You must "jump in the water" of life and people. Take a practical step this week to use your gifts to dive into the lives of people. Share your plan with a friend.

Session SEVEN

✔ TAKE IT IN (WATCH THE VIDEO)

Something as powerful as gifts usually has a _____.

FIVE CASE STUDIES OF SPIRITUAL GIFT ABUSE

1. "God spoke to me about you...you're supposed to..."

2. "Come into the back room/prayer room and I guarantee you will receive..."

3. "Every believer is supposed to receive this spiritual gift; it's the _____ that you're really..."

4. "I don't have a spiritual gift; I'm not worthy of one yet, but someday I hope..."

5. I don't care what the _____, I am God's prophet for this church and He has revealed to me that...

THE 10 MOST COMMON ABUSES OF SPIRITUAL GIFTS

1. Beware when spiritual gifts are used as a means of manipulation, power, or control in personal and/or church relationships. (1 Corinthians 12:4-7)

2. Beware whenever anyone claims to have the ability to give or bestow any particular gift if you follow their _____. (1 Corinthians 12:11)

3. Beware when any particular gift is made a _____ of spirituality, salvation, or other spiritual blessing. (1 Corinthians 12:29-30)

4. Beware when the focus of a church service, ministry, or religious event is on spiritual gifts and their manifestation rather than on the _____ of the gifts and His agenda for His church. (Ephesians 4:11-12)

5. Beware of _____ your gifts with anyone else's; it always leads to carnality. (1 Corinthians 12:11-18)

💬 TALK IT OVER

1. Of these first 5 abuses, which have you seen happen to others or had happen to you personally?

    _____

    _____

2. Read 1 Corinthians 12:11-18. What lessons can we learn about how the body of Christ is supposed to function in using spiritual gifts?

    _____

    _____

3. 1 Corinthians 12:18 says, "God has arranged the parts in the body, everyone of them, just as He wanted them to be."

    How have you done in accepting the way God made you and the gifts He gave you?

    _____

    _____

4. How can a person's insecurities make their gifts harmful and hurtful?

    _____

    _____

5. Read 2 Corinthians 10:12. What are some negative results that come from comparing ourselves to others? How big of a problem has this been for you personally?

    _____

    _____

6. What precautions can you and your group take to make sure you don't fall into any of these abuses?

_____

_____

✪ LIVE IT OUT

Several times this week read 1 Corinthians 12:11-18. Record your insights and observations about how the body of Christ is to function. Share your findings with a friend.

Session
EIGHT

PART 2

THE 10 MOST COMMON ABUSES OF SPIRITUAL GIFTS (CONTINUED)

6. Beware of any _____ position on spiritual gifts –
   i.e. "they do not exist" to "a spirit-filled Christian will have all the gifts."
   (1 Corinthians 12:1)

7. Beware of using your spiritual gift in the energy of the flesh to fulfill
   personal ego needs or impress other people. (1 Corinthians 13:1-3)

8. Beware of confusing spiritual gifts with _____
   as the evidence of spiritual growth and maturity.

EPHESIANS 4:13 (NIV)

until we all reach unity in the faith and in the knowledge of the
Son of God and become mature, attaining to the whole measure
of the fullness of Christ.

GALATIANS 5:22-23 (NIV)

22But the fruit of the Spirit is love, joy, peace, patience, kindness,
goodness, faithfulness, 23gentleness and self-control. Against such
things there is no law.

JOHN 15:8 (NIV)

8This is to my Father's glory, that you bear much fruit, showing
yourselves to be my disciples.

9. Beware that apparent "manifestations of the spirit" can be
   _____ by human schemes and demonic forces.

MATTHEW 7:22-24 (NIV)

22Many will say to me on that day, 'Lord, Lord, did we not prophesy
in your name, and in your name drive out demons and perform
many miracles?' 23Then I will tell them plainly, 'I never knew you.
Away from me, you evildoers!' 24"Therefore everyone who hears
these words of mine and puts them into practice is like a wise
man who built his house on the rock.

2 CORINTHIANS 11:13-15 (NIV)

[13]For such men are false apostles, deceitful workmen, masquerading as apostles of Christ. [14]And no wonder, for Satan himself masquerades as an angel of light. [15]It is not surprising, then, if his servants masquerade as servants of righteousness. Their end will be what their actions deserve.

10. Beware of viewing the discovery, development, and deployment of your spiritual gift either as an "optional exercise" or interesting but not serious responsibility.

EPHESIANS 4:8 (NIV)

This is why it says:
"When he ascended on high,
he led captives in his train
and gave gifts to men."

2 CORINTHIANS 5:9-10 (NIV)

[9]So we make it our goal to please him, whether we are at home in the body or away from it. [10]For we must all appear before the judgment seat of Christ, that each one may receive what is due him for the things done while in the body, whether good or bad.

YOUR SPIRITUAL GIFT ACTION PLAN

1. _____ to discover, develop, and deploy your spiritual gift in a local body of believers.

2. _____ seriously seeking divine guidance

3. _____ the gift passages in God's Word and corresponding handouts

4. Get quality _____

5. "_____" for six to eight weeks

6. Examine the _____ factor

7. Recognize God's evident _____

💬 TALK IT OVER

1. Which of the those 7 action items is the one that you need to commit to doing? Share that with the group.

_____

_____

2. Chip talked about the danger of ego when it comes to gifts. As you think about the spiritual gift you have, how could ego get in the way?

_____

_____

3. 1 Corinthians 13 is sandwiched right in between two chapters on spiritual gifts. Read 1 Corinthians 13:1-3. Why is this passage so important when it comes to spiritual gifts?

_____

_____

4. Chip spoke passionately about the importance of not only discovering our gift, but also developing and deploying them. Prior to this study, how would you have described your attitude toward your gift... casual? mildly interested? scared? passionate?

_____

_____

5. What has most impacted you through this study? What do you plan to do with what you have learned?

_____

_____

6. Through this study, what have you learned about others in your group? How can you see God using them to bless others?

_____

_____

⊘ LIVE IT OUT

Set aside an hour this week. Reflect on this study. What is it that God has been saying to you? How has He been trying to get your attention?

Then, as you think about what you've learned and how God has used this study in your life, write out your personal commitment to develop and deploy your gift. E-mail your commitment to a few friends asking them to pray for you as you put this into practice.

LEADER'S NOTES

Group Agreement

People come to groups with a variety of different expectations. The purpose of a group agreement is simply to make sure everyone is on the same page and that we have some common expectations. The following group agreement is a tool to help the group discuss specific guidelines together during your first meeting. Modify anything that does not work for your group, then be sure to discuss the questions at the bottom of this page. This will help you to have an even greater group experience!

WE AGREE TO THE FOLLOWING PRIORITIES

- Take the Bible Seriously — to seek to understand and apply God's truth in the Bible

- Group Attendance — to give priority to the group meeting
  (Call if I am going to be absent or late.)

- Safe Environment — to create a safe place where people can be heard and feel loved (no snap judgments or simple fixes)

- Be Confidential — to keep anything that is shared strictly confidential and within the group

- Spiritual Health — to give group members permission to help me live a godly, healthy spiritual life that is pleasing to God

- Building Relationships — to get to know the other members of the group and pray for them regularly

- Prayer — to regularly pray with and for each other

- Other

  _____

  _____

Our Game Plan

- Will we have refreshments?

  _____

  _____

- What will we do about childcare?

  _____

  _____

- What day and time will we meet?

  _____

  _____

- Where will we meet?

  _____

  _____

- How long will we meet each week?

  _____

  _____

How To Make This A Meaningful Experience For Your Group

BEFORE THE GROUP ARRIVES

1. **Be prepared.** Your personal preparation can make a huge difference in the quality of the group experience. We strongly suggest previewing both the DVD teaching program by Chip Ingram along with the accompanying parts of the study guide.

2. **Pray for your group members by name.** Ask God to use your time together to touch the heart of every person in your group. Expect God to challenge and change people as a result of this study.

3. **Provide refreshments.** There's nothing like food to help a group relax and connect with each other. For the first week, we suggest you prepare a snack, but after that, ask other group members to bring the food so that they share in the responsibilities of the group and make a commitment to return.

4. **Relax.** Don't try to imitate someone else's style of leading a group. Lead the group in a way that fits your style and temperament. Remember that people may feel a bit nervous showing up for a small group study, so put them at ease when they arrive. Make sure to have all the details covered prior to your group meeting, so that once people start arriving, you can focus on greeting them.

❤ TAKE IT IN (WATCH THE VIDEO)

1. **Arrange the room.** Set up the chairs in the room so that everyone can see the television. It's best to arrange the room in such a way that it is conducive to discussion.

2. **Get the video ready.** Each video session on the DVD has 3 components. During the first 2-3 minutes, Chip introduces this week's topic. Then, the group will watch the actual teaching content that Chip taught in front of a live audience. This portion of the video is roughly 20 minutes in length. Finally, Chip will then share some closing thoughts and set up the discussion topics for your group.

3. **Be sure to test your video equipment ahead of time.** Practice using the equipment and make sure you have located this week's lesson on the DVD menu. The video segments flow from one right into the next. So once you start the session, you won't have to stop the video until Chip has finished his closing thoughts and prepared the group for the first discussion question.

4. **Have enough materials on hand.** Before you start the video, make sure everyone has their own copy of the study guide. Encourage the group to open to this week's session and follow along with the teaching.

TALK IT OVER

Here are some guidelines for leading the discussion time:

1. **Make this a discussion, not a lecture.** Resist the temptation to do all the talking and to answer your own questions. Don't be afraid of a few moments of silence while people formulate their answers. And don't feel like you need to have all the answers. There is nothing wrong with simply responding "I don't know the answer to that, but I'll see if I can find an answer this week".

2. **Encourage everyone to participate.** Don't let one person dominate, but also don't pressure quieter members to speak during the first couple of sessions. After one person answers, don't immediately move on; ask what other people think, or say, "Would someone who hasn't shared like to add anything?"

3. **Affirm people's participation and input.** If an answer is clearly wrong, ask "What led you to that conclusion?" or ask what the rest of the group thinks. If a disagreement arises, don't be too quick to shut it down! The discussion can draw out important perspectives, and if you can't resolve it there, offer to research it further and return to the issue next week. However, if someone goes on the offensive and engages in personal attack of another person, you will need to step in as the leader. In the midst of spirited discussion, we must also remember that people are fragile and there is no place for disrespect.

4. **Detour when necessary.** If an important question is raised that is not in the study guide, take time to discuss it. Also, if someone shares something personal and emotional, take time for them. Stop and pray for them right then. Allow the Holy Spirit room to maneuver and follow His prompting when the discussion changes direction.

5. **Form subgroups.** One of the principles of small group life is "when numbers go up, sharing goes down". So, if you have a large group, sometimes you may want to split up into groups of 3-5 for discussion time. This is a great way to give everyone, even the quieter members, a chance to say something. Choose someone in the group to guide each of the smaller groups through the discussion. This involves others in the leadership of the group and provides an opportunity for training new leaders.

6. **Pray.** Be sensitive to the fact that some people in your group may be uncomfortable praying out loud. As a general rule, don't call on people to pray unless you have asked them ahead of time or have heard them pray in public. But this can also be a time to help people build their confidence to pray in a group. Consider having prayer times that ask people to just say a word or sentence of thanks to God.

☮ LIVE IT OUT

These simple suggestions will help you apply the lesson. Be sure and leave adequate time to talk about practical applications of the lesson. This is a great way to build group community.

Try these ideas together and hold each other accountable for completing them, then share the following week how it went.

A FINAL WORD...

Keep an eye on the clock. Be sensitive to time. Whatever is the agreed upon time commitment, try to stick with it. It is always better to finish the meeting with people wanting more rather than people walking away stressed out because the meeting went long.

Session Notes

Thanks for hosting this series called **Your Divine Design**. This practical series will help you and group to discover, develop, and deploy your spiritual gifts. Whether you are brand new at leading a small group or you are a seasoned veteran, God is going to use you. God has a long history of using ordinary people like us to get his work done.

These brief notes are intended to help prepare you for each week's session. By spending just a few minutes each week previewing the video and going over these leader notes you will set the table for a great group experience. Also, don't forget to pray for your group each week.

Session 1

YOU'RE A MASTERPIECE IN THE MAKING (1) 7

- If your group doesn't know each other well, be sure that you spend some time getting acquainted. Don't rush right into the video lesson. Remember, small groups are not just about a study or a meeting, they are about relationships.

- Be sure to capture everyone's contact information. It is a good idea to send out an e-mail with everybody's contact information so that the group can stay in touch.

- When you are ready to start the session, be sure that each person in your group has a copy of the study guide. The small group study guide is important for people to follow along and to take notes.

- The video lesson taught by Chip Ingram will be about 15-20 minutes in length. So, you will have plenty of time for discussion. Each session opens with Chip setting up the lesson. Then, the video will transition to his live teaching. And, at the end of the teaching Chip will come back and wrap up the session as well as set up the first discussion question for the group.

- Facilitating the discussion time. Several times Chip will ask you as the facilitator to lead the way by answering the first question. This allows you to lead by example and your willingness to share openly about your life will help others feel the permission to do the same.

- One of the discussion questions this first week asks some of the people in your group to share their personal conversion experience. Some people may not feel comfortable doing this, so don't single out anyone. If you know some in your group already, you might want to ask a couple of people in advance if they would be willing to BRIEFLY share their personal conversion story.

Session 2

- Why not begin your preparation by praying right now for the people in your group. You might even want to keep their names in your Bible. You may also want to ask people in your group how you can pray for them specifically.

- If somebody doesn't come back this week, be sure and follow up with them. Even if you knew they were going to have to miss the group meeting, give them a call or shoot them an e-mail letting them know that they were missed. It would also be appropriate to have a couple of other people in the group let them know they were missed.

- Each time your group meets take a few minutes to update on what has happened since the last group meeting. Ask people what they are learning and putting into practice. Remember, being a disciple of Jesus means becoming a "doer of the word".

- The first question this week asks people to share about somebody that God has used in your life to shape you and help you grow spiritually. As people share, make sure that they don't just share about the person, but they also share what that person did to influence your group member. You want to help your group see the potential impact of using our gifts to bless others.

- Live It Out. At the end of the study notes for each session is a section called Live It Out. This section has a couple of ideas or exercises that people in the group could do to deepen their experience with this teaching.

Session 3

- Did anybody miss last week's session? If so, make it a priority to follow up and let them know they were missed. It just might be your care for them that keeps them connected to the group.

- Share the load. One of the ways to raise the sense of ownership within the group is to get them involved in more than coming to the meeting. So, get someone to help with refreshments... find somebody else to be in charge of the prayer requests... get someone else to be in charge of any social gathering you plan... let someone else lead the discussion one night. Give away as much of the responsibility as possible. That is GOOD leadership.

- Think about last week's meeting for a moment. Was there anyone that didn't talk or participate? In every group there are extroverts and there are introverts. There are people who like to talk and then there are those who are quite content NOT to talk. Not everyone engages in the same way or at the same level but you do want to try and create an environment where everyone wants to participate.

- Follow up questions. The only thing better than good questions are good follow up questions. Questions are like onions. Each question allows another layer to be peeled back and get beneath the surface.

- Don't be afraid of silence. When you ask people a question, give them time to think about it. Don't feel like you have to fill every quiet moment with words.

- The last question this week asks the group to review the 7 motivational gifts that Chip talked about during the session. Then, the group members are asked to share which one most describes them. If people are unsure or feel like there are a couple that describe them, that's great. Remove any pressure that people feel to nail this down. Remember, we are just getting started.

- This would be a great week to really challenge people to do the Live It Out exercise. They will be challenged to do a little survey of 3 people that know them well. And, they are to ask this question; "As you have observed me, where do you think I am most gifted?" This can be a great help in people discovering their motivational gift.

Session 4

HOW TO DISCOVER YOUR PRIMARY SPIRITUAL GIFT (2) 25

- As you get the group together this week, do a check in from last week. Ask people if they did the Live It Out exercise. They were challenged to survey 3 people with the question "As you have observed me, where do you think I am most gifted?" Don't shame or embarrass people if they didn't do it, but encourage them to do it this coming week.

- Don't feel any pressure to get through all the questions. As people open up and talk, don't move on too quickly. Give them the space to what is going on inside them as they interact with this teaching.

- If your group is not sharing as much as you would like or if the discussion is being dominated by a person or two, try subgrouping. If your group is 8 people or more, this is a great way to up the level of participation.

- After watching the video tape, divide the group into a couple of smaller groups for the discussion time. It is good to get someone you think would be a good facilitator to agree to this ahead of time.

- There is a wide range of beliefs and understanding about spiritual gifts. It is great to have lively discussion and for people to share their opinions. However, be careful that the conversation doesn't become a debate.

Session 5

HOW TO DEVELOP YOUR SPIRITUAL GIFT FOR KINGDOM IMPACT (1) . . . 33

- You are now at the halfway point of this series. How is it going? How well is the group connecting? What has been going well and what needs a little work? Are there any adjustments you need to make?

- Confidentiality is crucial to group life. The moment trust is breached, people will shut down and close up. So, you may want to mention the importance of confidentiality again this week just to keep it on people's radar.

- The opening question this week is "Describe a time when you feel like God used you?" Without putting pressure on anyone, try to get everyone to answer this question.

- The fourth discussion this week is about our future judgment as believers. "Read about the Judgment Seat of Christ in I Corinthians 3:10-15 and 2 Corinthians 5:6-10. What can we learn from these two passages about our accountability for the stewardship of our gifts?" It is important to remember that this judgment is for believers only and is a judgment of reward. This is not a judgment to determine who gets into heaven. The primary question from God that we will answer at this judgment is "What did you do with what I gave you?" If you are unfamiliar with these passages you might want to look at notes in a study bible or read a commentary.

Session 6

HOW TO DEVELOP YOUR SPIRITUAL GIFT FOR KINGDOM IMPACT (2) . . . 39

- One way to deepen the level of community within your group is to spend time together outside the group meeting. If you have not already done so, plan something that will allow you to get to know each other better. Also, consider having someone else in the group take responsibility for your fellowship event.

- As Chip closes this week's session, he challenges your group to move beyond studying about gifts and diving in to "use" their gifts. As the leader of the group, challenge people to take a next step and get involved somewhere in using their gifts. Emphasizing the Live It Out section this week will also help people move into action.

- During Chip's wrap up this week he also challenges the group to consider serving your church as an entire group. Have some discussion about this and explore possible options for you to serve together. It will be a huge blessing to your church and draw you closer together as a group.

- As you begin this week's session, do a check-in to see what people are learning and applying from this series. Don't be afraid to take some time at the beginning of your meeting to review some key ideas from the previous week's lessons.

- Consider asking someone in your group to facilitate next week's lesson. Who knows, there might be a great potential small group leader in your group. It will give you a break and give them a chance to grow.

Session 7

WARNING: BEWARE OF SPIRITUAL GIFT ABUSE [1] 45

- Since this is the next to the last week of this study, you might want to spend some time this week talking about what your group is going to do after your complete this study.

- As this series winds down, this is a good time to plan some kind of party or fellowship after you complete the study. Find the "party person" in your group and ask them to take on the responsibility of planning a fun experience for the group. Also, use this party as a time for people to share how God has used this series to grow them and change them.

- During this session, Chip is going to talk about Spiritual Gift Abuse. Like any good thing that God creates, gifts can be distorted and abused. At the end of the session Chip will encourage people to share if they have personally experienced gift abuse. As the leader, seek to insure that the sharing is appropriate. The point is not too be overly critical or to attack people from our past, but rather to create a safe place where people can appropriately process how those experiences impacted them.

- Since some of the sharing could be a bit delicate, be sensitive to the hurt that some in your group may have experienced at the hands of other Christians. If you feel led, don't be afraid to stop and pray for group members after they have shared something personal and difficult.

- One of the discussion questions this week is going to have your group look at a longer passage in 1 Corinthians 12. Try to have a couple of extra Bibles available for people to use and follow along.

Session 8

WARNING: BEWARE OF SPIRITUAL GIFT ABUSE (2)

- Since this is your last session in this series, make sure that you have talked about what your group is going to do next. Also, consider taking a week or two break and doing a party/fellowship together. For some additional options for small group curriculum look at **livingontheedge.org**.

- At the close of this week's session, Chip is going to once again challenge those in your group to activate their gift. It would be a good idea for you to reinforce this and remind the group that the purpose of this series was not just to discover our gifts, but to also deploy them in building up the body of Christ.

- This final Live It Out exercise is a good one to help people commit to what they have been learning. The Live It Out section says "as you think about what you've learned and how God has used this study in your life, write out your personal commitment to develop and deploy your gift. E-mail your commitment to a few friends asking them to pray for you as you put this into practice."

Prayer and Praise

One of the most important things you can do in your group is to pray with and for each other. Write down each other's concerns here so you can remember to pray for these requests during the week!

Use the Follow Up box to record an answer to a prayer or to write down how you might want to follow up with the person making the request. This could be a phone call, an e-mail, or a card. Your personal concern will mean a lot!

PERSON	PRAYER REQUEST	FOLLOW UP

PERSON	PRAYER REQUEST	FOLLOW UP

PERSON	PRAYER REQUEST	FOLLOW UP

PERSON	PRAYER REQUEST	FOLLOW UP

PERSON	PRAYER REQUEST	FOLLOW UP

PERSON	PRAYER REQUEST	FOLLOW UP

PERSON	PRAYER REQUEST	FOLLOW UP

PERSON	PRAYER REQUEST	FOLLOW UP

PERSON	PRAYER REQUEST	FOLLOW UP

PERSON	PRAYER REQUEST	FOLLOW UP

What's Next?

More Group Studies from Chip Ingram:

Balancing Life's Demands
Biblical Priorities for a Busy Life

Busy, tired and stressed out? Learn how to put "first things first" and find peace in the midst of pressure and adversity.

BIO
How to Become An Authentic Disciple of Jesus

Unlock the Biblical DNA for spiritual momentum by examining the questions at the heart of true spirituality.

Culture Shock
A Biblical Response to Today's Most Divisive Issues

Bring light—not heat—to divisive issues, such as abortion, homosexuality, sex, politics, the environment, and more.

Doing Good
What Happens When Christians Really Live Like Christians

This series clarifies what Doing Good will do in you and then through you, for the benefit of others and the glory of God.

Experiencing God's Dream for Your Marriage
Practical Tools for a Thriving Marriage

Examine God's design for marriage and the real life tools and practices that will transform it for a lifetime.

Five Lies that Ruin Relationships
Building Truth-Based Relationships

Uncover five powerful lies that wreck relationships and experience the freedom of understanding how to recognize God's truth.

The Genius of Generosity
Lessons from a Secret Pact Between Friends
The smartest financial move you can make is to invest in God's Kingdom. Learn His design for wise giving and generous living.

The Real God
How He Longs for You to See Him
A deeper look at seven attributes of God's character that will change the way you think, pray and live.

Good to Great in God's Eyes
10 Practices Great Christians Have in Common
If you long for spiritual breakthrough, take a closer look at ten powerful practices that will rekindle a fresh infusion of faith.

The Real Heaven
What the Bible Actually Says
Chip Ingram digs into scripture to reveal what heaven will be like, what we'll do there, and how we're to prepare for eternity today.

Holy Ambition
Turning God-Shaped Dreams Into Reality
Do you long to turn a God-inspired dream into reality? Learn how God uses everyday believers to accomplish extraordinary things.

House or Home: Marriage Edition
God's Blueprint for a Great Marriage
Get back to the blueprint and examine God's plan for marriages that last for a lifetime.

What's Next?

More Group Studies from Chip Ingram:

House or Home: Parenting Edition
God's Blueprint for Biblical Parenting
Timeless truths about God's blueprint for parenting, and the
potential to forever change the trajectory of your family.

The Invisible War
The Believer's Guide to Satan, Demons and Spiritual Warfare
Learn how to clothe yourself with God's "spiritual armor" and be
confident of victory over the enemy of your soul.

Love, Sex and Lasting Relationships　　UPDATED
God's Prescription to Enhance Your Love Life
Do you believe in "true love"? Discover a better way to find love,
stay in love, and build intimacy that lasts a lifetime.

Overcoming Emotions that Destroy
Constructive Tools for Destructive Emotions
We all struggle with destructive emotions that can ruin relationships.
Learn God's plan to overcome angry feelings for good.

Rebuilding Your Broken World
How God Puts Broken Lives Back Together
Learn how God can reshape your response to trials and bring
healing to broken relationships and difficult circumstances.

Spiritual Simplicity
Doing Less · Loving More
If you crave simplicity and yearn for peace this study is for you.
Spiritual simplicity can only occur when we do less and love more.

Transformed
The Miracle of Life Change
Ready to make a change? Explore God's process of true transformation and learn to spot barriers that hold you back from receiving God's best.

True Spirituality
Becoming a Romans 12 Christian
We live in a world that is activity-heavy and relationship-light. Learn the next steps toward True Spirituality.

Why I Believe
Answers to Life's Most Difficult Questions
Can miracles be explained? Is there really a God? There are solid, logical answers about claims of the Christian faith.

Your Divine Design
Discover, Develop and Deploy Your Spiritual Gifts
How has God uniquely wired you? Discover God's purpose for spiritual gifts and how to identify your own.

Download the Chip Ingram App

The Chip Ingram App delivers daily devotionals, broadcasts, message notes, blog articles and more right on your mobile device.